Winter

SPY IT! SCORE IT!

Introduction

Winter is the season between autumn and spring, and in the UK, it spans the entire months of December, January and February. When the ground is covered in snow and ice, it's the perfect time to grab a sledge, find a snow-covered grassy slope, and have some fun! And then, when you can no longer feel your fingers, there's nothing better than returning inside to sit in front of the fire with a mug of hot chocolate to warm yourself up!

It's also the time when animals that aren't in hibernation are out, eagerly searching for food. Why not put up a bird feeder to help keep the birds well-fed? You might even see them visiting your feeder with their feathers puffed up to keep themselves warm!

So, wherever you are, and whatever you're up to, get spotting all things winter!

How to use your i-SPY book

Keep your eyes peeled for the i-SPYs in the book.

If you spy it, score it by ticking the circle or star.

Items with a star are difficult to spot so you'll have to search high and low to find them.

Once you score 1000 points, send away for your super i-SPY certificate. Follow the instructions on page 64 to find out how.

2

Winter is here

Look out for these signs of winter.

Robin

Although you can see these red-breasted birds all year round, they are easier to spot in winter because there are fewer leaves and plants for them to hide in.

10 POINTS

Frost

Tiny droplets of water freeze when the temperature dips overnight, and make plants look white in the morning.

5 POINTS

Winter is here

Dog wearing a coat

Some dogs are bred for warmer climates and need a coat to keep them warm during the colder months.

10 POINTS

Open fire/ woodburner

You don't have to get too close to an open fire or woodburner to feel the heat coming from the flames.

15 POINTS

Hot chocolate

A mug of hot chocolate is a comforting drink when it's cold outside.

Lip balm

This protects lips from the cold and wind, and often comes in different flavours.

Hot water bottle

A hot water bottle in a bed helps to warm it up and keep feet warm during the night.

Weather

There are lots of different types of weather in winter. They usually have one thing in common: they're cold!

Rain

Whether the rain is light drizzle or a heavy downpour, you will need your raincoat if you go outside in it.

Sleet

Sleet is frozen rain that has partially melted before it reaches the ground. It looks like slushy snow.

Snow

Each snowflake is made of tiny ice crystals stuck together, and no two snowflakes are ever the same. Snow can settle as a light dusting or a thick blanket.

30 POINTS

Hail

Hail is formed in thunderclouds and falls as balls of ice called hailstones. They are usually small, but can be up to 50 mm in size.

20 POINTS

Weather

Sub-zero temperature

When the temperature drops to below 0 °C, it is known as sub-zero. Look at an outside thermometer or a weather app to see a temperature below freezing

15 POINTS

Icy puddle

At sub-zero temperatures, water freezes to ice. Any puddles on the ground become frozen and very slippery.

20 POINTS

Frozen lake

If the temperature stays below freezing for long enough, the water on the surface of a lake will become cool enough to freeze. Even though it may look solid, it probably wouldn't be strong enough to stand on.

35 POINTS

Icicle

When drips of water freeze from an overhanging structure, the result is beautiful icicles.

25 POINTS

Freezing fog

TOP SPOT!

Fog occurs when the air near the ground is full of tiny droplets of water, like a cloud. When it is very cold, the fog that comes into contact with the ground or other surfaces freezes to create ice crystals known as rime.

50 POINTS

Ice scraper

This is used to scrape the ice off car windscreens on frosty mornings.

5 POINTS

Weather

Gritter lorry

When cold weather is forecast, gritter lorries spray salt onto roads. This helps to stop dangerous ice from forming on the surface of roads.

25 POINTS

Red sky

In certain weather conditions, the sky at sunrise or sunset can be an amazing red colour. This happens when dust particles in the air affect the light.

35 POINTS

Snow!

There is something magical about looking out of the window in the morning and seeing everything covered with a blanket of snow.

Snowman

As soon as there's enough snow, you will start to see snowmen appearing in gardens and parks. Choose a shaded spot if you're making one, and it will last longer when the weather begins to warm up.

25 POINTS

Snowball

A snowball fight is a good way to keep warm in the cold, snowy weather.

25 POINTS

Snow!

Sledge

If you head to a nearby hill or slope after a heavy snowfall, you might see people sliding down it on their sledges.

25 POINTS

Igloo

50 POINTS

TOP SPOT!

An igloo is a domed shelter made from blocks of packed snow. You need deep, wet snow to make one of these.

Snow shovel

A snow shovel is useful for clearing the snow from paths, pavements and driveways, to make them easier to walk or drive on. You might see one for sale in a shop or petrol station.

20 POINTS

Snowboard

Snowboarding is a popular mountain sport that requires a lot of snow and good balance. Score points if you see someone snowboarding on a dry slope, or in actual snow!

50 POINTS

TOP SPOT!

Snow!

Skis

Skiing is another popular winter sport. People sometimes ski on dry or indoor ski slopes in the UK.

TOP SPOT!

40 POINTS

Snow plough

When there is deep snow on the roads, a snow plough is attached to the front of a vehicle to clear a way through it.

TOP SPOT!

50 POINTS

Night sky

The dark evenings in winter mean there is plenty of time to observe the night sky and all the interesting things that are in it.

Sunset

You will need to look to the west at the end of a clear day to see the sun disappearing below the horizon. The time of sunset changes, getting a little bit later each day after the winter solstice on 21 December.

10 POINTS

Night sky

Canis Major

Finding Orion's belt will help you locate the constellation of Canis Major, Orion's mythical hunting dog. The belt points downwards to a bright star named Sirius, which is on the chest of the Canis Major dog.

30 POINTS

Orion

A constellation is a group of stars that make a recognised pattern in the sky. Many constellations have stories, or myths, about them. The constellation of Orion makes the shape of a mythical hunter. The easiest part to find is the 'belt', which is made up of three bright stars.

25 POINTS

Canis Minor

Orion's smaller hunting dog, Canis Minor, is northeast of Canis Major. It consists of only two stars, so has a less recognisable shape.

35 POINTS

Venus

Venus looks like a star but it's actually a planet. It is the second brightest object in the night sky and is visible low in the sky for a short time either before sunrise or after sunset.

30 POINTS

Venus

on

Full Moon

The Moon orbits the Earth and is the easiest object to identify in the night sky. Every 29 or 30 days, we can see the whole side of the Moon that is facing the Earth lit up by the Sun. This is called a Full Moon.

10 POINTS

Crescent Moon

At the beginning and end of each lunar month, the Moon is between the Earth and the Sun. The most we can see of the Moon from Earth is a very thin crescent.

10 POINTS

Quarter Moon

A Quarter Moon is when half of the side of the Moon that is facing us is lit up. This happens about every 14 or 15 days.

5 POINTS

17

Night sky

Taurus

The zodiac constellation of Taurus is seen as a bull shape, with two long horns. Orion's belt points northwest to the brightest star in Taurus.

30 POINTS

Gemini

Above Canis Minor, look for the mythical twins of the Gemini constellation. They are called Castor and Pollux.

30 POINTS

Geminid meteor shower

In the first half of December, close to the Gemini constellation, you might spot what look like shooting stars. This is the Geminid meteor shower, which can produce up to one hundred meteors an hour.

50 POINTS

TOP SPOT!

Lights

Look out for these types of light during the dark winter evenings.

Street light

Street lighting is essential for helping us find our way in the dark. Score for any street light which is lit.

5 POINTS

Outdoor light

Some houses have a welcoming light beside the front door.

5 POINTS

Fairy lights

These small lights strung together along a wire are used to add brightness both indoors and outdoors.

5 POINTS

Icicle lights

You might see a string of icicle-shaped lights hanging on the outside of a house or in a tree.

25 POINTS

Lights

Christmas light display

Towns, cities and shopping centres are lit up with bright displays at Christmas. Some people decorate their front gardens too.

5 POINTS

Reindeer lights

Look out for a lit-up reindeer among the Christmas displays.

15 POINTS

Candle

Candles are often burnt during winter to create a soothing glow, or you might see them on a birthday cake.

5 POINTS

In the garden

Although many plants and flowers don't grow in the winter, there is still plenty to look out for in the garden or your local park.

Bird bath

A dish of clean water provides birds with somewhere to drink, especially in freezing temperatures.

15 POINTS

Bird feeder

During winter it can be hard for birds to find food, so many garden birds will visit feeders for seeds, nuts and fat balls.

5 POINTS

Bird table

Some birds, like robins, prefer to eat from a table rather than a feeder. They love to eat mealworms.

10 POINTS

In the garden

Bug house

A bug house full of sticks or bamboo creates a hidey-hole for insects such as ladybirds, woodlice and solitary bees.

20 POINTS

Bare tree

Trees that lose their leaves in autumn are described as deciduous. They stay bare during winter, but will grow new leaves in spring.

5 POINTS

Evergreen tree

Evergreen trees such as conifers, fir trees and monkey puzzle trees keep their leaves all year round.

5 POINTS

Evergreen hedge

Hedges are great for providing food and shelter for wildlife. Some hedge plants keep their leaves through the winter, including privet, laurel and yew.

5 POINTS

Holly

Look out for the small red berries and prickly leaves on holly trees. Birds and small animals like to eat the berries, but these are poisonous to humans.

15 POINTS

Ivy

Ivy is a climbing plant that grows up walls and tree trunks. It has clusters of small, black, berry-like fruits during winter.

5 POINTS

TOP SPOT!

Mistletoe

Mistletoe is a parasite, which means it feeds off other trees. It grows in clumps on the host tree and is easy to spot in winter when the host tree has lost its leaves. If you don't see it growing on a tree, look out for it in the shops at Christmas.

40 POINTS

Snowdrops

These delicate little white flowers start to appear in January. They grow in small clumps that can carpet a woodland floor.

5 POINTS

Crocus

Crocuses flower towards the end of winter and are usually purple, yellow or white.

10 POINTS

Pansy

You might see colourful pansies planted in garden pots, hanging baskets or flower beds.

10 POINTS

Primrose

These small plants grow in woodland and in gardens. They flower in late winter in various colours including yellow, white, red, pink or blue.

10 POINTS

Winter jasmine

Winter flowering jasmine is a climbing plant that produces cheery bright yellow flowers from January onwards.

25 POINTS

Camellia

These plants have glossy, green leaves all year round, and bright pink, red or white flowers in late winter.

20 POINTS

Daffodil shoots

From mid-winter onwards you will see daffodil shoots growing out of the ground, usually in groups. They are a sign that spring is on its way.

Buds

Trees and plants that lose their leaves in autumn will start to get buds forming as winter nears its end. Score for any type of bud that you spot.

Birds

Many birds can be seen in our gardens, parks and lakes during the winter. See if you can spot any of these birds which live in the UK all year round.

Blackbird

Blackbirds like to sing from the tops of trees or hedges. Male blackbirds are black with an orange beak, while females are dark brown all over. Score 5 points for seeing either.

5 POINTS

Blue tit

These small blue and yellow birds are regular visitors to bird feeders.

10 POINTS

Great tit

Great tits are bigger than blue tits and have black on the tops of their heads. They often fight with smaller birds to keep them away from bird feeders.

 10 POINTS

Long-tailed tit

Their long tails and pinkish feathers make these small birds easy to recognise. You usually see them in groups, in trees, hedgerows and sometimes on fat ball feeders.

 35 POINTS

Birds

Goldfinch

This bird has a red face, black and white head and bright yellow wing feathers, so it is easy to identify.

20 POINTS

House sparrow

These small birds gather in noisy groups in gardens, parks and the countryside. The male has a black beak, grey head and white cheek, while the female is brown. Score 5 points for seeing either.

5 POINTS

Dunnock

Dunnocks are small, grey and brown birds that you will usually spot on their own, hopping around on the ground under bushes. Look out for their pinkish-orange legs.

20 POINTS

Woodpigeon

This large pigeon has a distinctive cooing call. It has grey feathers which are pinkish on its front, and a white band around its neck.

10 POINTS

Birds

Collared dove

A relative of the pigeon, the collared dove is a pale grey-brown colour all over, with a black collar round its neck.

25 POINTS

Magpie

These noisy black and white birds are easy to recognise. They are regular visitors to parks and gardens, where you may see them in groups.

5 POINTS

Coot

You will find these birds on freshwater lakes in parks and in the countryside. They are black all over apart from the white patch on their face and forehead. Their beak is also white.

30 POINTS

Pheasant

These large game birds inhabit open countryside, close to woodland. The male has a chestnut-coloured body with a green head and a red patch around the eye. The female is a mottled brown colour. Score 20 points for seeing either.

20 POINTS

Birds

Kestrel

If you see a small bird of prey hovering in the air near a roadside before diving down to catch its prey, you can be fairly certain it's a kestrel.

 35 POINTS

Mallard

This is the commonest duck in the UK. It can be found in lakes, canals and ponds, in towns and countryside, and even in gardens! The male is easy to spot with his green head and yellow bill, while the female is mostly brown. Score 10 points for seeing either.

10 POINTS

Mute swan

Mute swans are the only swans that live all year round in the UK. They are also the largest, and have orange and black bills.

25 POINTS

Grey heron

It's easy to miss a grey heron standing still beside a river, canal, lake or pond waiting to catch a fish, but it is unmistakeable when it flies off, because of its large size.

40 POINTS

TOP SPOT!

Animal behaviours

Certain animal behaviours are best seen or heard during winter.

Tawny owls *twit-twoo*-ing

If you're out in the countryside at dawn or dusk in December, listen out for the *twit-twoo* of the tawny owl. It won't be just one owl making this noise: it's a sign that there are two owls; the male going *twit* and the female replying with a *twoo*.

35 POINTS

TOP SPOT!

White mountain hares

Mountain hares swap their brown fur for white in winter, to help keep them camouflaged in the snow. This makes them easier to spot when there is no snow!

50 POINTS

Puffed-up feathers

When it's really cold, birds will puff their feathers up to help keep themselves warm. Score for any type of bird you see with puffed-up feathers.

25 POINTS

Red squirrels feeding

These rare animals often become tamer in winter as they search for food in peanut feeders. If you're lucky enough you will find them in certain woodland areas.

TOP SPOT!

50 POINTS

Animal behaviours

Foxes calling

Listen out for foxes making scream-like noises during their January mating season. You might hear them at night or in the early morning.

TOP SPOT!

40 POINTS

Starling murmuration

Starlings gather in their thousands at sunset and create this amazing spectacle of a giant swirling cloud of birds. It is thought that they do this to confuse predators.

35 POINTS

Animal prints in the snow

Before you start gathering snow to make a snowman, look out for any footprints of a bird or animal in the snow. Can you guess who made them?

35 POINTS

Spawning pike

You might see signs of these large, green freshwater fish mating in late winter. Look out for them thrashing about just beneath the surface at the edge of a lake or reservoir.

50 POINTS

TOP SPOT!

Christmas traditions

There are many traditions associated with Christmas, which you can look out for whether or not you celebrate it.

Christmas market

Wooden stalls selling gifts, food and drinks pop up in many towns and city centres during December.

 20 POINTS

Advent calendar

Advent calendars count down the days to Christmas with a treat behind each door.

 5 POINTS

Nativity scene

Nativity scenes depict the Bible story of the birth of Jesus. They usually include the shepherds and three wise men. You might see one in a shop, school or church.

20 POINTS

Santa Claus

Santa is unmistakeable in his red and white suit and with his white beard.

20 POINTS

Grotto

A grotto is a place where children go to tell Santa Claus what they want for Christmas.

25 POINTS

Elf

Santa's helper can usually be seen wearing green and red, with a pointy hat and pointy ears. You might see one in a Christmas display.

15 POINTS

Christmas traditions

Brass band

A brass band playing Christmas carols is a traditional sound at Christmas. You might see one in a town centre, raising money for charity.

35 POINTS

Carol singing

Carols are well-known songs that have been sung for centuries at Christmas time.

20 POINTS

Christmas card

One way to wish friends and family a merry Christmas is to write it in a card.

5 POINTS

Stocking

On Christmas Eve, stockings are traditionally hung up by fireplaces, to be filled with small presents overnight.

10 POINTS

Cracker

he usual way to start a hristmas meal is with bang! The person left ith the main part of e cracker wins the aper hat and ovelty inside, nd gets to ll the joke.

10 POINTS

Christmas traditions

Present

Giving presents is a way of showing people how much we appreciate them, and is an important part of Christmas.

5 POINTS

Christmas jumper

These festive clothes have all kinds of different colours and designs.

5 POINTS

Reindee[r]

Reindeer are best know[n] for pulling Santa's sleigh You might see a mode[l] of one in a display, or [a] real one at a farm park [or] outdoor grott[o]

25 POINTS

During December, houses, schools, shops and town centres are transformed with bright and colourful Christmas decorations.

Christmas tree

Christmas trees can be real or artificial, big or small, but they are all usually decorated with lights and ornaments. See if you can spot the four different types of tree decoration on the next page.

5 POINTS

Christmas decorations

Bauble ⬤ **5** POINTS

Pine cone ⬤ **5** POINTS

Angel ⬤ **5** POINTS

Star ⬤ **5** POINTS

Wreath

A festive wreath on a front door welcomes Christmas into the house.

10 POINTS

Garland

A garland may be made of foliage from a holly or fir tree, with added lights, bows or baubles. It can be used to decorate a mantlepiece, or to frame a door.

15 POINTS

Christmas decorations

Tinsel

Shiny, colourful tinsel adds instant sparkle wherever it is draped.

 5 POINTS

Wooden decoration

Score for any kind of Christmas decoration that is made of wood, whether it is hanging on a tree or standing on a shelf.

 10 POINTS

Inflatable

You might see a giant inflatable snowman or Santa in a front garden.

 15 POINTS

Santa sign

You might spot a sign like this outside a house. It helps make sure that presents are delivered there at Christmas.

15 POINTS

Fake snow

Fake snow made of polystyrene or fabric adds a wintry feel to a festive display in a shop window or shopping centre.

15 POINTS

Sleigh

Score for any sleigh you see, whether it is a small one hanging from a tree, one in a Christmas display, or a large one with Santa Claus on it!

15 POINTS

Food

Many different types of food and treats from around the world are sold in the shops during winter. See how many you can find.

Speculaas

TOP SPOT!

This spiced biscuit is eaten in the Netherlands and Belgium around the feast day of St Nicholas on 6 December.

40 POINTS

Stollen

This German sweet bread is filled with fruit and marzipan and baked at Christmas time.

30 POINTS

Lebkuchen

These soft biscuits contain honey and spices. They come from Germany and are often round or rectangular. They can also be heart or star shaped and coated in chocolate.

40 POINTS

Gingerbread house

Another traditional German Christmas treat is gingerbread, made into a house inspired by the story of Hansel and Gretel. It's fun to make your own and to decorate it with icing and your favourite sweets.

25 POINTS

Pannetone

This Italian sweet bread is usually baked in a tall, round tin and served at Christmas.

20 POINTS

Food

Mince pie

Mince pies have been eaten in Britain for centuries. They got their name because they used to contain meat, but the ones we see now are filled with sweet fruits and peel.

 5 POINTS

Chocolate coi

Coins made of chocolate and wrappe in foil, stamped with the designs real money, are often given Christmas. They were inspire by St Nicholas, who ga money as a gi

 5 POINTS

Candy cane

These sweet sticks with a curved end were first made in America. They are usually peppermint flavoured and striped red and white.

 10 POINTS

Roasted chestnut

The roasted nuts of the chestnut tree are a popular snack in Europe, Asia and North America.

 30 POINTS

Clementine

These small orange fruits grow in warm countries and are in season during winter.

 5 POINTS

Brussels sprout

Brussels sprouts are named after the city of Brussels in Belgium, though they are commonly grown in the UK. They are tastiest if they have been picked after a frost.

 5 POINTS

Turkey

Roast turkey is the traditional Christmas dinner. In the UK, about 10 million turkeys are eaten at Christmas time.

Christmas isn't the only festival celebrated during winter.

Hanukkah

The Jewish festival of light is usually celebrated in December. It lasts for eight days and involves lighting candles in a holder called a menorah. Score for any reference you see to Hanukkah.

50 POINTS

TOP SPOT!

Festivals, traditions and culture

New Year/Hogmanay celebrations

As the old year ends and the new year begins, it's a time to celebrate the good things that have happened and what is to come. You may see fireworks or other festivities starting early in the evening on New Year's Eve.

10 POINTS

Burns supper

The birth date of Scottish poet Robert Burns is celebrated on 25 January with a traditional Scottish meal of haggis, neeps (turnips) and tatties (potatoes). Score 25 points for any haggis you see, on a plate or in a supermarket or butcher's.

25 POINTS

Valentine card

The feast day of St Valentine on 14 February is a time for exchanging cards with those we love.

5 POINTS

Red rose

Romantic red roses are a traditional Valentine's Day gift.

15 POINTS

Heart-shaped chocolate

You might see heart-shaped chocolates around Valentine's Day.

10 POINTS

Festivals, traditions and culture

Lunar New Year celebration

Lunar New Year coincides with the New Moon that occurs between 21 January and 20 February each year. It is celebrated with lanterns, fireworks, food, and gifts or money given in red envelopes. You may see decorations in a Chinese restaurant or supermarket, or a reference to it in the media.

40 POINTS

TOP SPOT!

Pancake

Pancakes are eaten on Shrove Tuesday. This is always the day before the start of Lent, the time when Christians give up sweets or treats for the 40 days leading up to Easter.

10 POINTS

Pancake pan

A pancake pan is a round, flat, shallow frying pan which is designed to make the perfect pancake.

20 POINTS

Lemon

Lemon, along with sugar, is a traditional pancake filling, but there are lots of other things that are tasty in a pancake too.

5 POINTS

Clothes

Winter clothes are all about keeping us warm.

Earmuffs ◯ **5** POINTS

Fluffy socks ◯ **5** POINTS

Slippers ◯ **5** POINTS

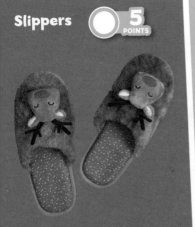

Bobble hat ◯ **5** POINTS

Down jacket

A jacket that is stuffed with feathers makes a very warm winter coat. Look out for the rings of stitching around the body and sleeves, which help to keep the feathers in place.

5 POINTS

Ski mittens

These padded gloves are made of waterproof fabric and are great for playing in the snow.

25 POINTS

Thermal T-shirt

A top made of soft, warm fabric gives an extra layer of warmth when the weather is very cold.

25 POINTS

Fingerless gloves

You might see these being worn by someone working outside who needs to use their fingertips, like a market trader.

15 POINTS

Clothes

Scarf

A scarf worn around the neck keeps the cold wind out.

 5 POINTS

Fur-lined hood

Look out for a jacket hood with fur around the edge.

 10 POINTS

Snow boots

Padded, waterproof boots are great for keeping feet warm in the snow and ice.

25 POINTS

Novelty hat

Score 30 points for any hat that has a fun design, such as an animal face or a Christmas pudding!

30 POINTS

Index

i-SPY How to get your i-SPY certificate and badge

Let us know when you've become a super-spotter with 1000 points and we'll send you a special certificate and badge!

Here's what to do:

✓ Ask an adult to check your score.

✓ Apply for your certificate at www.collins.co.uk/i-SPY (if you are under the age of 13 we'll need a parent or guardian to do this).

✓ We'll email your certificate and post you a brilliant badge!